GHOSTS

ON THE

BATTLESHIP NORTH CAROLINA

5/7/04

TO TIM

GHOSTS ON THE BATTLESHIP NORTH CAROLINA

Published by Bradshaw Publishing Company
P.O. Box 4564
Wilmington, NC 28406
(910) 793-2333
dbrad14@hotmail.com

Copyright © 2002 by Danny Bradshaw

4th Printing 10/03

ISBN 0-9717761-0-5

Printed by Wilmington Printing Company
Wilmington, North Carolina

Acknowledgements

There are a number of people that I would like to thank for making this book possible.

First I would like to thank Blonnie Wyche. She is the truc author of this book. She took what I scribbled down on a few pieces of paper and turned my words into a story worth becoming a book.

I would especially like to thank my good friend Jennifer A. King. Without her input, and her devotion to this project, it would never have become a reality.

Jamie Hobbs, of Capture Photography, did a wonderful job of obtaining just the images we wanted. Jennifer A. King also took photographs and produced the picture for the cover.

The Director of the U.S.S.N.C. Battleship, Captain David Scheu, gave his go ahead when I approached him. I am grateful to him for giving mc the opportunity to begin this project.

Kim Sincox, the Curator for the Battleship, has given wonderful support and has assisted in every way she could.

I must thank my cousin, Tommy Grant. He has been a part of this project from the start and always a great help.

My niece, Cheryl Cottle, is the reason this project was begun in the first place. Thank you, Cheryl.

I dedicate this book to my niece, Cheryl Cottle.
Overcoming many difficulties and hardships,
she has grown up to become a happy and
productive young lady. She is an inspiration
to me. I love her very much.

TABLE OF CONTENTS

Chapter 1

A GHOSTLY PROPOSITION

There are ghosts on the Battleship NORTH CAROLINA. I know that for a fact. I've felt their presence in icy arctic blasts of cold that penetrate a room and wrap around me like a polar wind loose from the wilderness.

I've heard their steps cross rooms and thud up and down the stairs, sometimes hurrying toward me as if to move me aside from where I stand, sometimes walking away as if, now that they had made themselves known, they could be done for a while.

I've seen their shapes, moving through a passageway or standing in a door. I have even looked into the face of one and know him to be young and strong and angry.

I've been living on the battleship and working as night watchman there since 1976. And how I came to have this job is the first story I'd like to tell.

My father and I ran a car dealership, which was a fine arrangement. We got along real well. Many nights I'd go over to the battleship to visit with a good friend who worked there. We played cards and talked about the day, mine at the dealership and his on the battleship. And he'd tell me about the ghosts.

Now when my friend John started talking about ghosts, I'd just shrug it off. I really thought he was kidding. He didn't look scared, or even serious. It was just part of the conversation.

On this particular night John said he was taking another job. "I've been on the ship for over five years, six nights a week, Danny," he said. "It's time to make a change."

"I'll miss our times together on the ship. You're a good poker player," I told him.

"Well, you don't have to miss the ship," my friend said. "I think if you want the job, you could take my place."

Here was a new idea. I was interested. I could work with my father during the day and stay on the ship at night. "Well, tell me the good and the bad, everything you know like the pluses and minuses of the job."

"You'll live right here on the battleship," he answered. "You'll have a bedroom and sitting area for your own use. You have to get up at 6:00 every morning to turn off the alarms so if you like to sleep late that's not so appealing. But the pay is not bad and you get free health insurance. You can build up a nice retirement."

He was speaking my language. The prospect sounded better and better as John talked, but I had the feeling he was holding something back. I was following him around as he checked doors to see that they were secure. We'd stop while he inspected a lock, then we'd move on to turn off the lights in that section of the ship. As he talked about what he was doing, I tried to read between the lines. We finally reached the top deck and I leaned against the railing.

"There's something you're leaving out," I pressed him.

He nodded. "Danny, there is one other thing." His expression turned very serious. "You know those jokes I make about ghosts? They're not jokes. There really are ghosts."

"You're telling me this ship is haunted by a ghost?"

"Ghosts, Danny. Ghosts. That's exactly what I am telling you." He leaned against the railing next to me and looked out across the Cape Fear River. "Danny, I know you may not believe me but it's true. There are ghosts on this ship."

"John, have you seen them?"

"No," he admitted. "I have never seen them, but I can tell when one is around. Things will start to happen. A light will be on that I know I cut off. A door will be open that I know I closed. Sometimes I can hear footsteps running in the halls at night."

"Well," I said, "if you are in your room asleep, how do you know that it's not somebody that just sneaked aboard the ship?"

"You know where the bullpen is?"

I nodded. The bullpen is located on the main deck on the starboard side of the ship. It was used as the crews' library during the war and was a gathering place for men while they were off duty. I'd been on the ship enough to know the layout of the public and private areas. John and I had played lots of card games sitting at a table in the bullpen.

"Danny, there is no way for anybody to get into that area at night because it is locked up. It's off limits to the tourists. For that matter, for almost anybody else. You have to go through an iron gate with a big lock to get in there." His fingers drummed against the railing.

"Since I've been here the bullpen's been used as a lounge and break area for the maintenance men. There have been times when I would go hang out in the bullpen at night. I would always turn the lights off and shut the door when I left. Only the next morning the door would be pushed open and lights turned on."

He'd stopped drumming and stuck his hands in his pockets. "I know you may think I just forgot to turn the lights off, but this has happened three, sometimes four nights in a row. Sometimes things will move by themselves."

"These things don't happen every night, do they?" I asked.

He shook his head. "No. You might go six months, or maybe a year, and nothing. Then all of a sudden things will start to happen." He held up his hand and began to count off on his fingers. "As a rule it will not be one thing." He pointed his index finger at the palm of his other hand. "Two or three things will happen in a row on the same night." He held up two more fingers. "Doors open. Lights go on and off. There are strange noises." He dropped his hands to his side. "When these events happen you know the ghosts are near."

"Well, what do you do when all this is happening?" I asked.

"I just stay in my room and hope morning will hurry up and get here. You have to deal with it the best way you can. Over the years I've heard a lot of scurrying about on this ship."

I started to walk away. Then I thought about the fact that John had been on that ship for over five years. How bad could it be if he'd stayed that long? I could always go out and sit in my car in the middle of the night, listen to music, maybe dream. That didn't sound too terrible. I like listening to a country western song, guitars plucking at the tune. Or maybe sway to a slow rock beat that moves around in my head till it gets into the soul.

I turned back to my friend. "If you're really leaving," I said, "and you think I can do the job, go ahead and tell me how to apply. Shoot, I can sleep through anything."

That was back in 1976. Except for a few months that I took off, on account of a woman, I've been on the job at the Battleship NORTH CAROLINA ever since.

So have the ghosts.

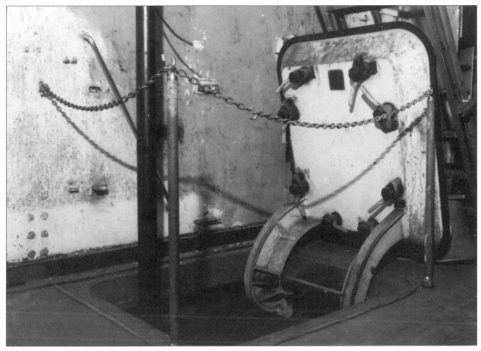

The hatch is carefully secured
in an open position
to give access to the ladder leading down
into the next level of the ship.

Chapter 2

FIRST ENCOUNTER

In the wintertime at the ship the nights are especially long. The ship closes to the public at 5:00. That's when I go on duty. Generally by 6:00 I am through with everything I have to do in closing up and setting the alarms. Then I watch television or listen to music, or get out a book to read. I do enjoy a good biography.

One night I was thinking about going down below deck to look for a small table for my living room area. I needed something to put my lamp on. And I will admit that I didn't want to go to the lower level of the ship by myself. I called my friend, John, to come over to help me look for a table.

"There is a lot of furniture and stuff stored on that

ship," John said. "As far as I know, you can use it up in your room or in the bullpen. I'll be glad to come over and we can look for something suitable for your room."

When he got there we each collected a flashlight and slowly began to make our way below. As we descended into the bowels of the ship, John started telling me about some of the sailors who were killed on the battleship during the war.

"A torpedo hit right between the two 16 inch turrets up forward," he said. "There was a group of men taking showers below deck when the torpedo ripped right through the area and killed them. One man standing on the main deck was thrown into the water and drowned. Of the ten men killed on the battleship, five were killed in that one torpedo blast."

We'd reached the bottom of one ladder and walked over to climb down to the next level. "I don't like being down here, Danny," he said. He pointed toward the ladder. "This is the area where that torpedo struck. But this is the place the tables are stored. We're sure to find one for the duty room."

Just ahead of us was a great hatch. The hatch there weighs at least 400 to 600 pounds. It is about four to six inches thick and made of iron. The way the hatch is angled back makes it impossible for it to just fall forward, even if the hook is pulled back. It is made this way because it is so heavy. If it fell on a man it would probably kill him.

There is a small ladder that leads down to the area

where the tables were stored. John and I started down toward this bottom level. Maybe it was the ring of our shoes on the ladder, or a ping from the ship's expanding and contracting metal as we moved deeper into the bowels of the ship, but I remembered that I had forgotten to set the alarm system. It really was important.

"John, do you mind if I go back up?" I asked. "I have to set the alarm. It will only take a minute."

"Sure," he said. He grabbed my arm and shook it. "Just come straight back."

I was back in less than ten minutes. When I got close to where I'd left John he was standing right there with a strange expression on his face.

"You look like you've seen a ghost," I teased.

He looked at me. "When did you get back?"

"Just now. When I spoke to you."

"We need to get out of here!"

"But we've got to open the hatch. John, we can't leave it closed."

Together we struggled to restore the hatch to its open position and secure it for access to the ladder. Then we moved out of there.

Up on deck John took a shuddering breath and blew it out with such force that he staggered back against the wall.

"What happened down there?" I demanded.

His words tumbled out in a great rush. "Danny, after you left, I climbed down the ladder and started looking around. I saw a table you might want. I started to reach for it." He held out his hands, ready to pick up something. "But I didn't get your table because just then I heard this loud crashing noise above me. I looked up. Danny, that big hatch had slammed shut." He swallowed, as if his mouth were too dry to keep on talking.

"Then what?" I again demanded.

"I almost panicked realizing I was trapped. That hatch is much too heavy for me to push open by myself. Then I remembered the ladder on the other side of the area. I crept over to the ladder. Thank God that hatch was open." He shook his head. "There is no way that hatch can fall by itself. Someone would have to take the hook off and then get behind it and push it shut."

"You're right," I said.

"Danny, the ghost didn't like us back in that area of the ship. I suggest you never go back down there by yourself."

Well, we talked a little more and then John said he had to leave. I walked him to the parking space where he'd left his car. He started to pull out, and then stopped.

Leaning out the window, he said, "I'm serious about you not going back by yourself. It is just too dangerous. The ghosts don't want us down there." His tires tossed up a little gravel as he pulled away.

I thought about what he'd said as I walked back up on the ship. The more I thought, the more I knew I had to go down below, just to see if I had the guts to do it. I started descending the same ladders that John and I had gone down together.

The closer I got to the hatch the more nervous I became. By the time I reached the open hatch I was getting real scared. I'd come back to prove something to myself, but I really did want a table to put my lamp on.

There was a lot of old furniture in the area. Tables and chairs and desks, some good and some not so good, filled one room. I looked at the tables and started to pick out one that would go by my chair upstairs.

I didn't hear any movement, but suddenly, right behind me, a voice screamed, "Get out of here!"

I jumped forward, almost falling into the open hatch. I started running as fast as I could. I hadn't gotten very far when I heard the hatch fall.

I made it out of there and to my room, but I was up all night. I didn't calm down until almost daybreak. Even listening to soothing country music didn't help too much. I am not as brave as I thought I was.

The ghosts on the battleship will make you think.

Since the bullpen was a place
for the men to relax off duty,
there was a desk where they could write letters.
Paper was provided for their use.

Chapter 3

PAPER TOSS

John came over often for a good game of cards. We'd play poker and talk. We solved a few of the world's problems and even a few of our own. We often talked about the battleship.

"We're lucky to be sitting here on this ship, you know," John said one night.

"How so?" I asked.

"Well, it was in '59 that the Navy decided to scrap her. After all the battles and decorations during the war there didn't seem to be any use for her at all." He shook his head. "Thank goodness for men like James Craig, here in Wilmington, who pushed for her to be saved.

"And thank goodness for the appeal to school

15

children to give their pennies to the fund to save the ship. One third of the money raised to bring the battleship to Wilmington was given by school children."

We get a lot of children visiting the ship. They come with parents and grandparents, with school classes and youth groups. It's always a pleasure to have children and young people wanting to know about the Battleship NORTH CAROLINA.

Then one night John got to talking about the ghosts.

By now I'd been on the battleship for a couple of years. I'd had no more encounters with the ghosts like the one down on the lower level of the ship. Not once had I seen anything out of the ordinary. At night there were the usual creakings and groanings of metal. If the day had been extremely warm and the night air turned really cool, the expanding and contracting of metal caused loud popping noises. That was to be expected. The sudden noise of shifting structure could startle you, but it wasn't scary.

"You know," John said as he shuffled the deck, "once that ghost is around, he will not stop with one thing."

"What do you mean?" I asked.

John fanned the deck of cards across the table. Then he picked up a card and slapped it down. "He'll do something. Like he'll turn out the lights." John slapped another card. "He'll do something else. Like he'll make noises. He'll keep on and on, trying to really scare you."

"Well, I haven't seen or heard anything since the night we went to get the table. I'll just wait him out, whoever or whatever he is," I said. "And by the way, I brought a little table from home to use. It works fine."

It was the spring of 1978 before I found out what John meant about several things happening when the ghost got started. I was staying in the bullpen instead of in my room because the air conditioning was better there. I had closed the ship up that night and was sitting on the couch talking on the phone. All of a sudden I heard what sounded like paper crumpling. It was that sound when you take a sheet of paper and scrunch it into a ball before you try a shot at the wastebasket. I looked across the room toward the sound.

Two sheets of paper were balling themselves up. I mean, right there, in the air, two sheets of paper were balling themselves up like someone had them in their hands squeezing them, getting ready for a good toss. Then the paper wasn't there. I could hardly believe what I was seeing. And then not seeing.

I glanced toward the clock. It was 8:00, which was time for a show I liked to watch, so I turned the television on. Every now and then I'd glance over where the paper had been tossed in the air, but nothing else happened then. By the time the news was coming on I'd convinced myself that I'd heard a rat scratching, and that I'd never really seen paper being balled up ready to sail toward the wastebasket.

I turned off the lights but left the television on for the comfort. The room was basically dark. A friend called and I was talking on the phone when the area around me

17

began to get brighter. It was like lights coming up on stage, getting brighter and brighter, while the audience waits for the first actor to come out and speak his lines. I half expected to see a costumed performer walk into the room. The brighter the room got the colder it got. The air was so frigid I began to shiver. Quickly I said good-bye to my friend and hung up the phone.

The brightness and the chill only lasted fifteen or twenty seconds. Then the light dimmed until only the glow from the television lit the room. The chill went back to the normal coolness that the air conditioner gave the bullpen.

I got my stuff and went out to my car in the parking lot. I stayed in my car the rest of the night. I listened to the radio for a while. Some rock and roll played low through the speaker. "Ain't No Sunshine" didn't help my nerves and "What's Going On" wasn't much more soothing. I eventually drifted to sleep with the beat of the music, my head arched back on the seat.   But I did not go back aboard ship until the sun was full up. Whoever wanted to play in the bullpen had his space. I didn't want to crowd him any.

That incident happened so many years ago. I have never seen anything like that paper trick since.

The ghosts played other kinds of mischief as time went on.

The bullpen of the battleship,
both during the war years,
and now,
has many uses.

Chapter 4

COLD AND EERIE

My friend, Mike, called one night in the fall of 1982. "The wife's out of town, Danny," he said. "How about if I bring a deck of cards to the ship and we'll play poker."

Mike had done this plenty of times before. As far as the ghosts were concerned, he did not believe in them. He didn't want to hear stories about lights going on and off, or hatches slamming shut, or even about dark passages on the ship. I respected his opinion about the ghosts, so we never discussed them.

That fall night we decided to play cards in the bullpen. In this large room was a big table with chairs, a large couch, and a nice refrigerator. There was also a bathroom — or head, in navy terms.

That night the temperature outside was about seventy degrees or so. I did not have the air conditioner or heat on in the bullpen and it was very comfortable.

Mike got there and we started playing poker about eight o'clock. I held a good hand. Then Mike held a better hand. I bluffed him some and he paid me back with the next hand. The conversation was easy, normal everyday stuff.

We'd been at the game for about thirty minutes when I started to get an uneasy feeling. Something wasn't right in the room. I tried not to pay attention at first, but the vague nervous feeling got more powerful. The hair on my arms tingled and I rubbed my hands from my wrist to elbow. The feeling intensified. Mike was still talking, but I had pushed back my chair from the table, looking about the area.

There was something evil in the room. Something hateful and dreadful, like I had never felt before, spread through the bullpen. The horror of it ran all through me.

Mike stopped talking in mid-sentence and looked around. A strange look came over his face.

"What's wrong?" I asked him, in what I hoped was a conversational tone.

"Oh, it's nothing," he answered, but that frightened look stayed on his face. He kept turning to look toward the door.

I thought he must be feeling the same awful feeling that I was, so I asked him again, "Mike, what's wrong?"

Before he could answer, a sudden gust of cold air filled the entire room. It was not like a normal cold. I shivered inside from an eerie arctic blast that wrapped about the room as if it would freeze us in place.

Mike gripped the edge of the table and looked again toward the door.

"There's one in here, isn't there?" he whispered.

"Sure is," I said in an undertone, my voice as quiet as Mike's.

"Danny, there is something very evil in this room." His words got louder and louder until he was yelling. "Let's get the hell out of here." He stood so quickly that his chair overturned, but his hands still hung on to the table.

"Sit down, Mike. Wait for a minute." I was trembling with cold and fear, but I somehow knew we shouldn't rush out and leave the coldness behind. We had to be the ones to stay and let the ghost leave first.

Mike's feet weren't moving, but he was still standing. "That cold wind came over me. That great gust of cold air came all over me. Did you feel it?"

I nodded.

He righted his chair and sank into it. "Danny, it's like something poisonous is in here. Like something dark. Like something very wicked will happen."

"Just wait, Mike." It took all of my strength to say that.

"This cold air is all over me." His voice quavered. "I can't take this any longer. Danny, It's freaking me out."

"I'm feeling the same thing. Just sit tight." I knew that was what we had to do, and I had to calm my friend. "Do something for me."

"What?" he snapped.

"Just as soon as this feeling leaves you, I want you to let me know."

"Danny, I'm not staying here much longer." He was perched on the very edge of his chair. If I'd yelled boo at him, he'd have fallen in the floor.

The refrigerator door opened. There was no one there to open the door except an unseen presence. We both stared at the lunch meat I'd bought to make sandwiches and the cans of Mountain Dew I had stacked on the shelves. Then the refrigerator door closed. About twenty seconds passed as Mike and I sat in silence.

Suddenly the room temperature shot right back up to normal. The chilling feeling left just as quickly as it had come.

"Danny, it just left."

"Yes, I know."

"Now can we get out of here?"

After we got down to the parking lot Mike said, "Danny, I owe you an apology. You know I don't believe in ghosts." He paused a moment. "Or at least I didn't believe in ghosts. I sure do now. That was the scariest feeling I ever had in my life."

"Don't feel bad, because it was the scariest thing I have ever had happen to me."

Mike left, driving slowly out of the parking area. He

didn't wave.

That fall night was the first time that I had really felt the strong presence of the ghosts. Over the years I have learned that the ghosts can be in the room and I won't ever know it unless something happens. Sometimes a door will open. Sometimes a light will turn itself off. Sometimes something in the room moves by itself. When I'm here by myself on this great ship, it can be quite unnerving. I've tried to give the ghosts their space and trust they'll respect mine.

It was a long time, after that night, before Mike came back for a poker game.

A light from a porthole shows up brightly on a dark night.
To see a face peering out,
when no one is supposed to be on the ship,
is discombobulating.

Chapter 5

UNEXPLAINED COMPANY

A frightening, and at the same time most thrilling experience with the ghosts, happened in the winter of 1989.

Jennifer, a really good friend, called about six o'clock one Friday evening. "I want to come over and bring you supper," she said.

That sounded like a winner to me and I told her so. "When were you planning on coming over?" I asked.

"I'll be there at seven. Danny, will you meet me in the parking lot? I have several dishes."

Right over the phone I could almost smell the chicken frying. Going down to the parking lot for a home-cooked meal was the least that I could do.

About 6:45 I locked my room door with the padlock as I always do and climbed to the upper deck to cut the alarms off.   As I was walking down the ramp to meet Jennifer in the parking lot, I saw her drive in.

Jennifer got about parallel to my room. She stopped, looked up toward the ship and started blowing her car horn. I was already in the parking lot, looking at her and thinking that she would have to see me. She sat there blowing the horn for what seemed like an eternity.

Finally she drove down to where I was standing. She rolled down her window and called, "Who's your company?"

"You're my company, Jennifer. I'm sure glad to see you."

"Someone is in your room."

"Jennifer, there's no one in my room. There's no one on the ship. All visitors left two hours ago and I've finished locking up for the night."

She just stared at me.

"Why were you honking your horn, anyway?" I asked. "I was waiting here when you pulled into the parking area."

She took a deep breath. "Danny, when I drove into the parking lot and stopped by your room I blew the horn. When I looked up at your room the curtain pulled back and a head appeared at the porthole. The face just stared out. I thought it was you but it just kept staring."

She touched her own face, as if to make sure it was still there. "Finally the head pulled back from the

28

porthole. The curtain closed."

Jennifer turned in the seat to look straight at me. "That's when I drove on down by the ramp and saw you standing in the parking lot."

I took her hand. "There is no one in my room," I assured her. "I just left my room and locked the door behind me. There really is no one there."

"Get in the car, Danny. I'll show you which porthole it is, because I did see somebody."

I got in the car and Jennifer backed up till she was opposite my window. Just as she stopped I opened my door and got out to look up toward my room. "Jennifer, see? All the curtains are closed."

She started to say something and stopped with her mouth open. One of the curtains in the living room area pushed aside and a head appeared in the porthole.

Jennifer found her voice. "Do you see that?" she screamed.

I saw it but could not believe it. Chills started running up and down my arms. My heart started beating faster and faster. I was scared, but I was excited too. I was seeing one of the ghosts. After all the years of hearing them, feeling their presence and hearing stories about them, I finally was *seeing* one of the ghosts himself. He was there for only a minute, but I saw him clearly - a shadow form in the porthole.

As I watched, he moved his head back at an angle. Then he closed the curtain.

Jennifer was babbling about ghosts and battleships

29

and empty parking lots, but I couldn't respond to her right then. I was thinking about a ghost being in my room where I slept. That was most unsettling to me. As excited as I was to see the ghost, I needed to sort through the different feelings that were invading me.

Jennifer got real quiet. Then she said, "Danny, it was a ghost."

I nodded.

"I've got to go."

I didn't blame her at all. We said good night and she turned the car around and drove away.

As I walked back up on the ship I was nervous. Once I got to my room I found the padlock still secure on my door. I unlocked it and went in my room. Everything was just as I left it. There was no way for anybody to get in or out of that room. So what had I seen at the window?

That was one of many sleepless nights I've had aboard the battleship. That night was a little worse than some, because it wasn't long before my stomach was growling. Jennifer had driven away with the fried chicken. She's a great cook. For a brief second I wondered if the ghost would have shared supper with me. Then I decided not.

Now that I had seen a ghost, would there be other sightings?

The stairs leading from one level to another
on the ship are fairly wide and steep.
It's not hard to move quickly on the steps
when speed is required!

Chapter 6

SOUND AND LIGHT AND A BLOND-HAIRED MAN

June, July, and August were the hardest months for me to work when we had the Sound and Light Spectacular. The battleship stayed open until 8:00, when regular tourists had to leave. The fascinating show, which included lights, the sounds of battle, and the history of the ship, began at 9:00. By then, even on the longest days, it was full dark for the electrifying fireworks display that ended the Spectacular.

After the Sound and Light Spectacular was over it took a while for everybody to leave. It was usually 10:30 before the last car had pulled out of the parking lot and I could start closing up. I had to lock up the doors around the gift shop area and then go aboard the ship. Below deck was an electric power box with a switch I had to cut off. I hated going down there late at night. It was always a little spooky below with no one else around and all the lights turned off.

I'd been below deck hundreds of time and nothing had ever happened, but I always had a feeling that some night it would. On that particular July night of 1992, the Show had gone real well and there was a large crowd of people. It was almost 11:00 before everybody finally left the area and I could start closing up. I locked all the doors around the gift shop and went below on the ship to cut the power switch off.

It was even hotter than usual for mid-summer. The temperature below deck must have been close to 100 degrees. I wiped my face with my shirttail and followed the beam of my flashlight as I made my way down the passageway.

Just as I reached the power box a gust of cold air hit me. I felt a hand on my shoulder. The feeling of fear that gripped me was unimaginable. My knees buckled but I willed myself to spin around. I shined my flashlight down the passageway.

No one was there, but the hand lifted from my shoulder. I heard the sound of someone wearing hard-sole shoes walking away from me in the dark. I pointed my flashlight in the direction of the footsteps.

Just a few feet away from me was a young blond-headed man looking off to the side. What was most frightful was that the light passed right through him. He turned his head and stared at me. It was an angry look, as if he wanted to say, "Don't shine that light at me." Or maybe he was thinking what I was: "Leave me alone." Then the young man disappeared.

The only thing I could think about was getting up to the main deck. That would prove much more difficult than I counted on. The stairs that I came down, and that I had planned to use going back up, were in the direction the ghost was walking. I was not about to go that way. I decided to go to the starboard side of the ship where there was another set of stairs leading out. When I got to the stairs I heard the sound of the same kind of hard sole shoes coming down the steps toward me. That's when I started to panic. I ran all the way to the forward port of the ship where there were two more sets of stairs leading up to the main deck. Out of breath, and sweating like crazy, I all but flew up those steps and got up on the main deck.

I didn't stop there. I ran right off the ship and got in my car. I drove to the river's edge and turned on the radio. Roy Clark was singing about being young yesterday. I let Roy and the music calm me down some, wondering how old I might be in the morning. I stayed in my car all night and didn't venture aboard the ship till the sun was well up.

A lot of people were sorry when the Sound and Light Spectacular ended production in 1995. It was a splendid show with the lights and fireworks that lit up the sky to simulate battles the old battleship had seen. She had thrown her share of fire power at the enemy. She had taken her licks and forged ahead with pride. But the dead still haunted her decks. No amount of light seemed enough for them.

Now I had seen another of the ghosts. This one was very different from the one who peered from my porthole. I am glad not to have those late night rounds after the Sound and Light Spectacular.

PHOTOGRAPHER JENNIFER A. KING

The van, moving away from the ship,
picked up a passenger one night.
When a ghost hitches a ride, it can cause problems!

Chapter 7

THIS GHOST TOOK A RIDE

One of the most unusual and frightening things happened to a special lady that I was seeing at the time. She called one night to tell me she was going to a party, but she wanted to come by and spend some time with me before she went. That was fine with me. I always wanted to see this favorite person.

I met her down in the parking lot about eight o'clock. She was all dressed up and bubbling about the friends she would see at the party. I told her how really great she looked and she thanked me. We sat in her van and talked for a while.

"I'll call you when I get home," she said. "Tell you all about who was there and what we did at the party."

I watched her drive out of the parking lot. Then I went back up on the ship, set the alarms and went to my room. I hadn't had time to settle in with my book when the phone rang.

"Danny! Danny! Danny!" This hysterical voice was yelling my name over and over.

"Who is this?" I asked.

The voice kept repeating my name and something about the ship. I finally recognized the voice of my girlfriend.

"Sweetheart, calm down and talk slower so I can understand what you're saying," I pleaded. "What is wrong with you? Were you in a wreck? Where are you?"

She took a deep breath and answered my last question. "I'm at the service station just over the bridge."

"Are you hurt?"

"No. I don't think so."

"You don't think so?" I was glad she was speaking slower, but she still didn't sound like her usual self.

"What happened?"

"Oh, Danny, the strangest thing. When I drove out of the parking lot this awful cold feeling just gripped me. I have never felt such a strange cold in my life. The further I drove the worse it got. I even turned on the heater."

Was it one of the ghosts from the battleship? This was the first time I'd known the ghosts to leave the ship and follow someone. Of course, I did not say anything out loud about ghosts. My friend was already far too upset. Then I realized she was still talking.

". . . not the really bad part, Danny. Just as I got to the top of the bridge, out of nowhere, everything in the back of my van started flying around, slamming against the side panels. It was like someone was in the back just picking everything up and slamming everything against the inside of the van."

Her voice was getting panicky again. "There were cans flying and books going through the air. The jumper cables twisted and whirled around. Even the beach chair folded and unfolded and smashed against something. I thought I was going to get hit with a flying object right inside my own van. I started screaming." And she started screaming.

I talked into the phone as calmly and quietly as I could. I asked again if she were hurt.

"No," she wailed.

"If you're at the service station, can the people there help you?"

She wasn't screaming now and I heard her take a shuddering breath. "There was a man here standing by his car when I pulled in. I hollered to him for help."

"Did he help you?"

"I told him I thought someone was in the back of my van. He opened the door and climbed in to check it out for me. Then he stepped out of the van and said, 'Lady, there is no one in there.' So I thanked him and told him I was grateful for his help. And I was. But Danny, there was something in my van! There was!"

So we talked for a while about what she wanted to

do. She was pretty calm by now, although I thought she could panic again if I said the wrong word. I was being very selective with any advice or suggestions about how she should handle the situation. What I wanted was for her to come back to the ship for her own safety.

Finally she said, "Danny, I think I might just come back there if that is okay with you."

"That is probably a good idea," I said. "I'll be waiting for you in the parking lot."

She pulled up a few minutes later. She was shaking and her voice had a quaver in it. She jumped out and grabbed my hands. "That cold feeling is still in the van, Danny. That strange cold that won't get warm is still there!"

I squeezed her hands and let my thoughts go over all she'd told me. It had to be a ghost. The invading cold and objects flying without an explanation said a ghost was at work. Was one of the ghosts from the ship jealous of my attentions toward this particular lady? Did a ghost get lost? Was he trying to get away from this location and take up residence somewhere else? There was no reason to scare her further so I didn't say any of my thoughts out loud.

Finally she pulled her hands away from mine. "I'm going home now, Danny. I'll call you when I get there."

She called about thirty minutes later.

"Any more problems?" I asked.

"No," she answered. "But the funniest thing was this. As soon as I drove out of the parking lot the temperature in the van went back to normal and that eerie feeling left. It sounds crazy, I know. I don't believe in the supernatural. Danny, you know I don't. But this experience sure was unearthly."

She took a deep breath. "Danny, could there have been a ghost in my van?"

That's when I told her that the battleship is haunted.

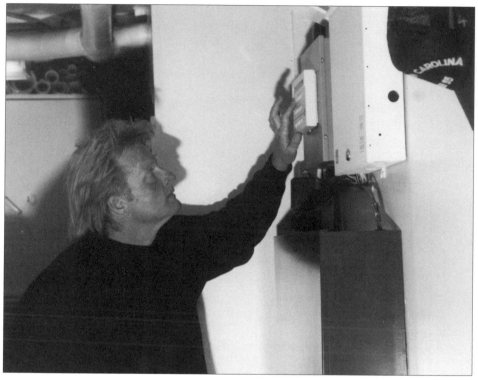

I have only a short time to switch alarms on or off.
I punch in the numbers
even when a ghost is yelling at me!

Chapter 8

GHOSTS DON'T JUST MAKE NOISES!

When I tell the stories of the ghosts to visitors touring the battleship, they ask a lot of questions. Some believe in spirits and some don't, but they all ask if the ghosts say anything. In my years on board the battleship there have been times when one or another has spoken.

My first experience of hearing a ghost speak was when a yelling voice screamed at me: "Get out of here." That had been when John and I were below deck looking for a table.

My next experience of hearing a ghost speak occurred when the new gift shop building had just opened. The gift shop is a large, beautiful building with a new auditorium, snack bar and viewing area. My job is to make sure everyone is out of the building after visitor's hours, and then lock all the doors before going aboard the ship for the night.

It was only the second night of locking up the new building and I was still working out the route I wanted to use. I made the rounds and was sure everyone was out. I then locked the front doors and started walking down the viewing hall. Suddenly a screaming voice, just behind me, yelled, "Hey, what are you doing?"

I whirled around to see who had yelled at me. No one, that I could see, was there.

The voice had come from the other end of the viewing area near the auditorium. I thought to myself that no visitors could be there because I had just locked up all the doors, but just to make sure I doubled back to check it out. As I walked down the hall a feeling that I was not alone came over me. Right behind me the same voice screamed, "Why are you here?"

I literally froze in my tracks. I know that's an old saying, but for that particular moment I could not move. A coldness moved about me and I felt chills through my whole body.   My heart was racing so fast I thought it might burst from my chest and I felt like I might pass out.

Then I realized that if I did pass out I'd be lying in the viewing hall for everyone to see when someone found keys in the morning and got the doors opened. Now that would be a horrifying sight for the staff and tourists!

I got myself together, in spite of the terror I felt, and ran outside and around the building. I took a deep breath and began to feel a little more safe. That feeling didn't last long.

I'd finished checking all the doors, knowing how important it is to have the buildings secure. I turned to go up to the ship. Just behind me the same voice shouted, "Don't come here again!"

I couldn't believe it. The ghost was following me all around the building. It was as if I could not get away from him. I have never been so scared in my life.

"Get to my room" was the only thought in my mind. "Get to my room and lock the door and stay very quiet." Surely this ghost, if he wanted to haunt the new gift shop building, wouldn't follow me to my room on the ship.

I made certain every lock was secure and every alarm was turned on, but I did it on the double. By the time I locked my own door and dropped down in my big chair, I was breathing almost normally again. I turned on the television, thinking I could take my mind off of the events. Ghosts talking to me is not high on my list of priorities. But I kept listening. I'd turn down the volume on the television and cock my head to catch sounds. That was one long night I spent aboard the battleship.

The next time a ghost spoke to me occurred some four years later. It was a soft spring morning. There wasn't much traffic yet, at 6:30 in the morning. A pair of mockingbirds were having a concert in a tree near the gift shop and I stopped for a moment to listen to their song.

The first thing I have to do to start my morning rounds is go up to the assistant director's office, located in the captain's cabin, and turn off the alarm system. That particular morning I went in the captain's cabin and unlocked the door. As I pushed it open I reached for and turned on the light switch. I took one step towards the assistant director's office.

"Get back," a deep voice shouted at me.

I was taken completely off guard. I tried to step back and tangled up my feet so completely that I almost fell. Even as I righted myself I knew the voice came from the same area where the alarm system is located.

Now that system is set up so that once I open the door to the captain's cabin I have only forty-five seconds to turn the alarm off. If I don't, it will go off and send a call to the police station. I had no choice except to go to the office and turn off the alarm.

As I entered the office I felt the cold envelop me. It was the same sensation I had encountered with the ghost in the bullpen years before.

How I could ever explain to the police that a ghost had stopped me from reaching the system I did not know. My hands were shaking violently but I got that alarm system switched off. I stood, hugging myself against the cold.

"Get back now!" a voice screamed just behind me.

I ran out of the door and down to the main deck. I still had to go below to cut the lights on. Reluctantly I descended and made my way to the switch boxes. All was quiet in the bowels of the ship and I heard no more voices that morning.

After I'd finished opening the ship that morning I gathered my things and left, not saying a word to anyone about what had happened. As I pulled out of the parking lot I heard the mockingbirds still warbling their tunes.

There is continuing repair aboard the battleship.
Recently a new teak deck,
to replace the old and worn deck, was laid.
The carpenters do not usually hammer at night.

Chapter 9

TAP, TAP, TAPPING

It was very cold that night in mid-January 1990. A brisk wind was blowing off the Cape Fear River, fanning the flags, whistling through the rigging, howling down the stacks. I zipped up my heavy jacket and pulled on my gloves. I rushed to close up so I could get to my room where it was nice and warm.

As I walked past the bullpen I heard a tapping noise. It was like someone with a hammer was tapping along the wall. A carpenter might make a noise like that if he were looking for a stud in the wall. I knew it wasn't caused by the wind because here in the bullpen noises don't penetrate from the outside.

I opened the door to investigate. The tapping

stopped. I shook my head, closed the door and finished making rounds.

When I got to my room I turned on the television to watch the news. The tapping started again. This time the noise was coming from my bedroom, right above my bed. For two or three minutes, long enough for several commercials to run on the screen, the tapping continued. Then it stopped.

Well, I thought, do I have a construction worker repairing something on this cold night? Is he finished yet?

Construction of the Battleship NORTH CAROLINA was authorized by an Act of Congress and passed in June 1936. Hundreds of men worked to build the great ship. While the building moved slowly ahead, Germany invaded Poland, Denmark, Norway, the Netherlands, and France. Japan invaded China and threatened expansion across the Pacific.

In June 1940 the NORTH CAROLINA was launched at the New York Navy Yard. Governor Clyde R. Hoey of North Carolina was the speaker at the ceremony.

Even after the launching of a ship, much construction must be completed. Then the shakedown period, where ship and crew work out any problems, begins. The ship returned to the New York Navy Yard often during the shakedown phase. Radio commentator Walter Winchell, seeing the great battleship's comings and goings, dubbed her "The Showboat," using the name of the popular musical then appearing on Broadway.

The men of the NORTH CAROLINA proudly accepted

the name. If "mis'ry's comin' 'round," as one of the songs from the Broadway show said, then they would have the battleship ready to meet the enemy.

The tap-tapping had stopped. I figured the ghost had had his fun and now he'd go away. Not so. The next program had come on the television when the tapping started again. By now I was more angry than scared. It was much too cold to spend the night in my car listening to the radio. I was determined to have the comfort and warmth of my own bed.

I went into the bedroom. The tapping continued. I stood by the bed and yelled, "Stop right now!" To my surprise, the noise stopped.

I went back to my program, got ready for bed and had a restful night's sleep. And I have never again heard the tap, tap, tapping of a hammer against the walls.

Doors lead into and out
of many sections of the ship.
Tourists learn to step over the raised frames.

Chapter 10

TOURIST ATTRACTION

I am not always by myself when one of the ghosts decides he wants his presence known. A spirit can manifest himself in various ways and in numerous places. And sometimes, it seems, certain people or situations bring out a need for an apparition to appear.

One such occasion happened in the spring of 1993. I made my announcement over the public address system telling the tourists that the ship was closing up for the night. After I locked up the doors around the gift shop area I went aboard the ship to cut the lights off.

Still on board the battleship was a family from Virginia. The man, his wife, and their two teenage sons, were on the deck looking around. I explained to them that we were closing and I was cutting lights off and readying the ship for the night.

"But we really just got here," the man said. "We've seen nothing of the ship at all."

The boys were mumbling about how much they wanted to see at least some parts of the ship. It seemed to mean a great deal to them.

"Well," I said, "you can walk with me while I finish closing the ship. We'll be going in some areas that might be a little dark and scary."

"Sounds like fun," said one of the boys.

"Yeah," said the other boy. "Mom? Dad? Let's do it!"

I could tell they were enjoying themselves. I don't usually do tours, but I do know a bit about the ship. I told them something of the history and how the Battleship NORTH CAROLINA came to berth in the Cape Fear River.

"How many men were killed on board the ship?" one of them asked.

"Only ten men were killed during the whole war," I told them.

Then they asked, jokingly, "Do you ever hear from any of them?"

"If you're asking me if the ship is haunted, the answer is yes."

They wanted to hear more. We'd finished the rounds and the ship was secure for the night. I invited them to the bullpen.

We sat around a big table with six chairs. The

family settled in. They asked me questions and I told them some of the stories of ghosts on the ship. We'd been there about twenty minutes or so when I began to feel something was not quite right. The feeling is hard to explain, but some sense of fear or anxiety is always present when one of the ghosts is about to manifest himself.

I could tell that the family was becoming quite uneasy. "You can stop me any time," I said.

"No, don't stop," said one of the boys. "We want to know more about the ghosts."

That was when the ghost made his presence known. The empty chair moved back from the table, scaring everybody.

"Don't do that again," the father yelled at the boy sitting next to the seemingly unoccupied chair.

"Dad, I didn't touch that chair," the boy pleaded. "It just moved."

The chair moved again. No one at the table was close enough to have manipulated it. I think it was obvious to all of us that the ghost was in the bullpen.

The wife was shaking and started screaming, "I want to get out of here! Get me out of here!"

The husband took her hand and they stood up.

"Don't worry," I told them. "We'll get out right now."

I fast-walked them off the battleship and out to the parking lot. All the way I tried to reassure them that everything was going to be fine.

Once we were off the ship the father said, "I've

never been so scared in my life." He shook my hand. "It wasn't your fault, I know. Thank you for taking us around and showing us everything. But I don't think I want to come back any time soon."

"How do you stay here all by yourself?" the wife asked.

"When the ghosts are roaming around, I don't," I answered. "I spend lots of nights in my car."

Just before he climbed in the car the older teenager whispered to me, "That was cool!"

I just nodded and waved them out of the parking lot. Cool this boy didn't know!

PHOTOGRAPHER JAMIE HOBBS

I do enjoy a cold Mello Yello or a Mountain Dew.
Here, in the Visitor's Center, I can select what I want to drink.
Double doors lead to the outside of the Center.
At night objects from the room reflect in the glass.

Chapter 11

THE PRICE OF A SODA

After the experience with the tourist family in the spring the spirits evidently felt they had succeeded in making their positions clear. I didn't know what their messages were, but they seemed to. The summer and fall seasons of 1993 were quiet for the ghosts on the ship.

One winter night that year I was watching television in my room and realized that I was thirsty. I didn't have anything to drink in my refrigerator so I gathered up some change for the machine and went down to the gift shop to get a soda. As I put my money in the coin slot I heard someone run right behind me. I whirled around. Of course there was no one there.

I got a second soda from the machine. Swinging

the cans back and forth in my hands, I was ready to go to the ship and my room.

Suddenly the double glass doors to the gift shop began to shake violently like someone was trying to get out. Chills ran up and down my arms and face. This time I'd had no warning that one of the ghosts was around. I think that scared me as much as the fact that he was so near without me feeling his presence before he started his pranks.

I ran towards my room. I didn't know if I were being followed and I didn't turn around to find out.

The commercials were over and the next program was starting on the television. I settled in with my soda. I listened for noises but I didn't hear anything before I went to bed. It wasn't really cold that night so I'd left the hatch leading to the outside of my room open. I don't like to be closed in.

About 5:00 in the morning I was awakened by loud pounding footsteps near my room. The heavy strides stopped just outside my door. For a brief moment all was quiet. Then the clamoring steps ran right through the open hatch and down the stairs leading below deck.

I had to go down those same stairs to cut the lights on for the tourists. I still had an hour before I had to go down to the panel box where the light switches are. That at least gave me some time to calm down. I admit I was nervous about it. I stayed there under the warm covers a while, waiting for the steps to return.

Finally I pulled myself from bed and got ready for

the day. I had no choice, really. The lights had to be turned on. I went down the stairs, opened the panel box and cut on the lights. I started back up. I was almost at the top when, from the bottom of the steps, I heard the same sound of running. The footsteps were coming up behind me.

I was so scared I almost fell. I bounded up those stairs, taking two or three steps at the time. I slammed the hatch shut and ran outside where it was just beginning to get light. Oh, it was such a relief to get outside from the dark ship and see daylight!

I thought about that encounter with the ghost for days. Was he thirsty? Did he want a swig of my soda? Did the hum of the drink machine and the thud of the can spilling down the chute disturb him? For the first time I really wondered about cause and effect. Facts are stubborn and I didn't have any. I just know the ghosts are there. And this one sounded like he was in a hurry.

For the next several nights I hardly slept at all.

My sitting room, with my chair and the television,
was once part of the officers' quarters.
The room is quite comfortable.

Chapter 12

THE GHOST WANTS MY ROOM

John had told me some of his experiences with the ghosts when he was night watchman on the battleship. "Most of the time, Danny," he had said, "the ghost will not stop at just one prank. He'll do two or three tricks before he stops his mischief."

I'd been thinking about John, that winter day of 1992. Almost everything he'd told me about working on the ship had been right on the mark. He had only been here for five or six years. I was starting my sixteenth year of making the rounds. Lots of changes had taken place at the ship. The gift shop had been expanded to a much larger building. The parking lot was about the same but a lighting system had been installed. There were always continuing ship repairs. I'd greeted countless thousands of tourists. I'd turned on lights and turned off lights more times than I could count. I knew the insides of that vessel as well as anyone. The one thing that did not change was the appearance of the ghosts and their antics.

The ship closed, that particular winter day, at 5:00. By 6:00 I was through closing up the ship and setting the alarms for the evening. I walked into my room and locked the door, heading for the refrigerator. Behind me I heard the doorknob turn.

I spun around to see the knob turning as if someone could compel a locked door open. I walked over and grabbed the knob. It didn't turn under my hand as I held on to it. I opened the door and looked up and down the passageway. No one was there. I hadn't expected them to be, not really. A ghost was roaming the halls tonight. As I have done in the past, I just shook my head and blocked the incident out.

I poured a soda and drank it while I straightened my room. Then I went in to take a shower. I was all soaped up when the water turned very cold. I looked at the hot water handle to see it turning to the off position.

"He's in the shower with me," I whispered to myself.

I turned the hot water back on and started to rinse. Before I had all the soap washed away the hot water handle began to turn off again. This I could not take. I got out of the shower and dressed. But I was determined not to get chased out of my room. It was very cold outside and I had no desire to spend the night in my car.

I knew the ghost was in the room and I was scared. I figured he would soon leave me alone. But on this night the ghost must have been particularly restless, because he did not stop with the doorknob and the shower handle.

I heated up my supper and sat down to eat. Suddenly my drink turned over and spilled onto the floor. That made me angry and I said so, in no uncertain terms, to the ghost. He left me alone while I refilled my glass and finished eating. I settled down with a book.

When it was time for "Jeopardy" to come on television I got up and switched on the set. I'd hardly gotten settled back in my chair when the television turned itself off. I got up and turned it back on only to have the screen blank out again. For the third time I tried to watch answers and questions from one of my favorite shows. For the third time the television turned itself off.

"Okay, mister," I said. "Have the room."

I grabbed my pillows and blanket and went up to the captain's cabin. I slept on the captain's couch the rest of the night. Nothing bothered me there and I had no more problems, that night, with the ghosts.

Like I said, it was cold that night. I guess the ghost just wanted my warm room. I sure let him have it.

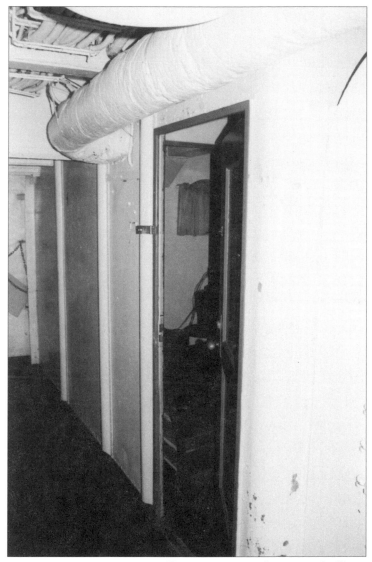

The door from my room opens onto a long passageway.
A person, or a ghost,
standing at the door,
would be able to see into the room
and up and down the corridor.

Chapter 13

THE LOOK

My cousin Tommy never comes over to the ship after dark. "Too creepy for me," is his explanation.

He had asked me many times how I could stay on the ship at night. "You sleep here. You eat here. You live here. Have you ever thought about changing jobs?"

"Not really," I answered. "I like my job."

I was surprised when he called this particular night and said he wanted to come over to discuss some family business.

"You're coming tonight?" I asked. "At night?"

"Well, we need to get this little problem taken care of now and I'm working tomorrow," Tommy said.

"Come on."

A few minutes later I met Tommy at the ramp and we went to my room to hang out and talk. We got the family matter taken care of and then just chewed the fat for a while. After about an hour I could tell that he was getting a little nervous. He squirmed in his chair and turned around to look behind him. His eyes darted back and forth like he was watching for something to appear. The strange part was that I was feeling a little uneasy myself.

I walked Tommy off the ship and to his car, where we said good night. "Don't know how you do it, Danny. I wouldn't stay on this ship at night for anything." He drove away in a hurry.

I watched him pull out on the highway and went back up to my room. My door was open! It was chilly that night and my heater was on. If that wasn't enough, I always close and lock my door when I'm not there. Then the eerie feeling, like I'd gotten in the bullpen years ago, the unearthly feeling I'd felt in many other places on the ship, surrounded me.

Inside the room the television was turned off. I knew I'd had it on when Tommy and I left to walk down to the parking lot. I shook my head and went on through to the bathroom.

I heard the television come back on, blaring out the voices at a volume I'd never use. I hurried across the room to turn the sound down. Then I stopped, mid-stride.

The ghost appeared by the door. This was the same ghost who had been below deck the time I was cutting off the power switch. The blond hair and the build told me that it was the same figure that I had seen then.

He looked at me. There was a blank appearance to his face as he stood there, gazing at me. It was an expression I could not read. Then he disappeared.

I was horrified. I turned off the television. I turned off the heat. I grabbed my jacket. I ran out the door and off the ship.

I was out of breath when I got to my car. I slid into the seat and locked the car doors and tried to calm my breathing. For a while I didn't even reach over to turn on the radio.

When I'd settled down some I found a station that was playing 80s country. "Don't Close Your Eyes" made me think I might never close my eyes again for fear of seeing that blond-headed young man staring at me. And the Judds singing "Mama, He's Crazy" seemed to be talking about me. I clicked off the station and leaned my head on the seat rest, knowing I would be awake all night.

I stayed in the car till the sun came up. Some nights are more frightening than others. But I always go back to the battleship.

EPILOGUE

I can't believe it has been over twenty-five years since I first started my job at the Battleship NORTH CAROLINA. When I began working here I intended it to be only a few years. After working on the ship for a while I enjoyed the fact that it was beginning to feel like home. For the most part I am alone. I like it that way. There is no one around to bother me. I have my own room on board where I can keep my belongings. I like the feeling of both working and living on the battleship.

There are some things that I dislike about my job. These are things that I never imagined that I would have to deal with. Of course, I am referring to the ghosts.

In the past there have been many times when I considered quitting my job. I am on a ship that is so big that it had the capacity to hold twenty-three hundred fighting men in time of war. I am walking alone down dark passageways late at night. Suddenly I hear the chilling noise of metal expanding and contracting. The noise goes on all night. I lie awake wondering if a noise that I just heard is the ship settling or if a ghost is roaming around in the ship's darkness. These incidents happening night after night can really unnerve me after a while.

I have people say to me, "Danny, how can you stay on that big haunted ship at night by yourself?"

I wonder that myself sometimes. It is surprising even to me. My encounters with the ghosts have lessened over the past few years. I have no idea why. Maybe after all these years the spirits have grown used to me. Maybe they know that I plan to stay on here until I reach retirement age.

Perhaps the ghosts are planning something more horrifying. Something deep down tells me that might be the case. I pray not. However I know that I can handle it. After my personal experiences with the ghosts I can deal with anything they plan to throw my way.

The Battleship NORTH CAROLINA is my home.